This book is dedicated to all the children of the world who love to read but have no easy access to books.

The Rat Family - An African Folk Tale
Henry Kayongo-Male, PhD

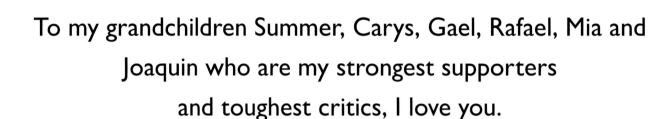

To my grandchildren Summer, Carys, Gael, Rafael, Mia and Joaquin who are my strongest supporters and toughest critics, I love you.

ISBN # 978-0-9983169-0-1
Book designed by Heather Rule Grady, Insit, Denver, CO
Illustrated by Home Plan Architecture Company, Uganda
Child Psychology Consultant is James Roger Nsereko, MS

African grandparents by tradition told short stories to children in the evenings by the fireside. The stories were full of real-life messages of courage, discipline and respect for elders and tribal traditions. This oral tradition was intended to develop youngsters into useful, mature members of society. It should be preserved.

Once upon a time, there was a rat family that lived happily in a peanut field.

They had a nice, safe underground nest built right in the middle of the field.

The peanut field belonged to an elderly peasant farmer, his beautiful wife and their two wonderful sons.

Every morning the father rat went out
with the two little pups and dug up
some peanuts for lunch.

Every afternoon the little pups went out
into the field to play. Soon they also
learned how to dig up whole peanuts
from the ground, shell them and
eat the seeds.

One day the little pups got very close to the farmer's house.

They heard the farmer talking to his sons about harvesting the peanut field.

Frightened, the pups ran home in a big hurry. The father rat asked, "What is the matter?"

Breathless, the pups explained that they heard the farmer tell his sons to prepare for the peanut harvest. "If the peanuts are going to be harvested, shouldn't we prepare to move to another home?" the pups asked.

"What did he say exactly?" the father rat asked.

"The farmer told his sons to ask the neighbors to come and help with the harvest," they replied.

The father rat responded calmly, "Do not worry at all. Go on playing in the field and have fun as usual."

Two days later, the father rat told the pups
to sneak back to the farmer's house
and listen to what the farmer
had to say.

They went as close to the house as possible. This time, the pups heard the sons tell their father that the neighbors had refused to help with the harvest. The father told the sons to ask their cousins if they would be willing to help with the harvest.

The pups ran home and told the father rat that the neighbors had refused to help with the harvest and that the father had told his sons to ask their cousins for help. The father rat told the pups once again not to worry.

"Go on playing in the field and have fun as usual," he said.

A few days later the pups
  went back to the house to
    listen to what the farmer and
      his sons were up to. The sons
        told their father that the cousins had
          also refused to help with the harvest.

The father then
told his sons, "Since the neighbors and the
cousins have refused to help with the
harvest, then we will have to
do it ourselves."

The pups ran back to the nest. They told the father rat that the farmer and his sons had decided to harvest the field themselves. The father rat, finally concerned, responded, "It is time to pack up and leave! We must get out of here fast!"

Confused, the pups asked their father, "But, why now?" The father rat explained to them that when the farmer was counting on others to do his work, it was clear that it would not get done.

"But when the father decided to depend on himself and his sons to do the work, I knew it was time to leave because the field was going to be harvested this time," said the father rat.

He continued, "It is not a good idea to seek help right away for something that you can do.

Take the first step yourself and maybe someone will help you along the way."

Self-reliance is a cornerstone of the African culture.
It is instilled in children at a very young age.